RAPHAEL SAPORTA

A Basket in the Reeds

ILLUSTRATED BY H. HECHTKOPF

PUBLISHED BY
LERNER PUBLICATIONS COMPANY
MINNEAPOLIS, MINNESOTA

AN
OUTSTANDING
SELECTION
FROM

Israel

First published in the United States of America
1965 by Lerner Publications Company, Minneapolis, Minnesota

Library of Congress Catalog Card Number: 64-25640

his story happened many, many years ago.
In those days there was a small nation, the
Hebrew people, and they lived in the land of
Egypt.
They were all one family, descended from their
ancestor Jacob. Jacob had also had another
name, given to him by an angel of the Lord,
the name "Israel."
His descendents were called "The Children
of Israel."

And the Children of Israel were wise and industrious.
They built houses and planted fragrant gardens.
They made beautiful clothes.
They had many sheep, cows, horses, and donkeys.

The Children of Israel tended the soil. They sowed and
harvested, had tasty bread, and abundant fruit, wine, oil,
milk, and honey.
And they had many, many wise and beautiful children who
helped their fathers and mothers at home and in the fields.

In those days there was a wicked king in Egypt. He was called Pharaoh.

His great palace stood on the bank of the river Nile.

Pharaoh was a bad king, an evil king.

He hated the Children of Israel.

One day Pharaoh said, "All the people of Israel shall be my slaves!"

And so it was.

All became the slaves of Pharaoh.

They were slaves to Pharaoh in the land of Egypt.
From morning until evening they toiled. It was hard work, back-breaking labor.
Every day they sweated in the clay pits making bricks.
They performed every kind of difficult work in the houses and every kind of laborious work in the fields.

Slaves. . . slaves. . . slaves. . .
The Egyptian overseers stood and cracked their whips. They whipped the people to make them work faster.

The Egyptians harnessed the Israelites to wagons to pull heavy loads.

They tied them to plows to plow the soil.
They put them to work in the valleys stamping clay.
They made them work in the blazing sun making bricks.
They made them work in the hills cutting rocks.
They made them drag the building blocks and pillars for the pyramids and palaces of Pharaoh.
They made them work without resting, without stopping for breath.
The Israelites slaved until they died.

"The work is hard," the Children of Israel sighed.
"The yoke is heavy."
"We have no more strength to suffer," the Children of Israel cried.

One night Pharaoh had a dream.
A lamb came out of the Nile and went into Pharaoh's palace.
It stood beside the huge pillar which held up the building.
It butted the pillar ten times —
thump — thump — thump.
Crash!
The building swayed; the building collapsed.
Its walls crashed down with a great noise onto Pharaoh and
onto Egypt.

Panic seized the Egyptians. People ran to and fro in fear and confusion.
They screamed and fell over each other.
The sun darkened. A black crocodile was swallowing the sun.
It was dark and gloomy all around.
There was heavy darkness over all the land of Egypt.
Only far off, remotely in the distance, could any light be seen.

Who were those people there, in the light?
There, in the light, were the Children of Israel.
They were marching, stretching out their arms, straightening their bodies and leaving their hard work.
Crowds of them were dancing, singing, and shouting in great joy.
The Children of Israel were going out of Egypt!

In the morning Pharaoh arose.

He wiped the cold sweat from his face. . . It was a dream.

He was frightened, and called all his magicians and wise men.

He told them his dream. The magicians listened.

They shook their heads, wrinkled their brows, and patted their beards.

What did the dream mean? The wise men of Egypt could not explain it.

But one man was there who was older and wiser than the others.

He said, "The lamb our Pharaoh saw in his dream stands for a little boy.

A woman of the Children of Israel will give birth to a little
boy.
When the boy grows up, he will make war against Pharaoh
and lead the Israelites out of Egypt."

Pharaoh was angry.
He said, "That will never happen!
All the little boys of the Children of Israel must die!"

Then and there he arose and commanded his people:
Cast every male-child that is born to them into the river!
Throw every little boy born to an Israelite family into the
Nile!"

Then bad and bitter days came to the Children of Israel.

Pharaoh's men passed through the quarters of the Israelites.
They went into the yards and into the houses.
They watched through the windows, peeked through cracks,
listened at key holes.
They came into the rooms, broke things, and searched.
They looked in all the corners and in every hiding place.
If they found a baby boy, they snatched him from his mother's
arms and threw him into the Nile.

In one little house far from Pharaoh's palace, an Israelite family lived.

Amram was the father, Yoheved the mother.

They had a son and a daughter, Aaron and Miriam.

One night the family was sitting in the light of a burning candle.

They were sad, very sad.

The candle flame rose and fell, rose and fell, and shadows danced on the walls of the house.

Father Amram sighed and said, "Our life is hard in the land of Egypt.

The Egyptians beat us, and make us do back-breaking work.

They don't let us rest.

And now our troubles are even greater. The Pharaoh has said 'Every son that is born, ye shall cast into the river.'

What shall we do? Where shall we go?

The other members of the family remained silent.

They bowed their heads in sorrow.

Suddenly Miriam rose and said joyfully.

"I had a dream last night. In the dream, we had a new baby boy.

The boy took a stick in his hand and went to Pharaoh.

He hit the palace ten times —

thump — thump — thump.

Crash!

The Pharaoh's palace rocked and collapsed.

It fell with a great noise onto Pharaoh and onto Egypt.

There was darkness and gloom in all the land of Egypt.

But for us alone a great light shone.

Far off, a pillar of fire as high as the sky moved before us.

And we walked behind the fire and the light.

We left the house of bondage and went out of the land of Egypt.

The day of redemption is near.

We shall not always be Pharaoh's slaves. We shall go out of slavery to freedom."

The candle flame rose. It lit up the house with a great light, and Miriam's eyes sparkled.

Father Amram kissed her on the head and said, "Be blessed, my daughter. Perhaps what you said may come to pass. We can only hope your prophecy will be fulfilled."

The members of the family raised their hands and prayed, "Oh God, take us out of this house of slavery. Send a good angel to save us from Pharaoh."

That year Yoheved gave birth to a son, a baby with beautiful eyes.

When he was born, the house filled with light.

Grandmother and Grandfather and all the relations and members of the family came to help Mother Yoheved with her work. They stood around the little baby, saw the light shining from him, and they could not look long enough at his beauty.

Mother Yoheved cried and said.

"My poor little baby! Why did I give birth to you?

Soon the Egyptians will come and take you out of my arms.

God, have mercy on the child!"

While she was nursing the child, the sound of horses' hooves
was heard.
"The Egyptians! The Egyptians are coming! The Egyptians!"
The warning passed from one Israelite house to another.
People whispered to each other.
There were knocks and secret signs.
Hide the little boys!
The Egyptians went from house to house, knocked on the
windows, and shouted,
"Is there a baby boy in here? Is there a baby boy in here?"
The Egyptians came into their street. They marched from
house to house.

Yoheved pressed the infant to her heart.
She was trembling. She shook with fear.
Her face was burning. She sheltered the baby in her arms.

No! She would not hand over her child to the Egyptians!
The Egyptians! The Egyptians were coming closer.
Soon they would reach Amram's house.
They came into the yard, kicked the door and shouted through the window.
"Is there a baby boy in here? Is there a baby boy in here?"
One Egyptian beat on the locked door with a club.
"In the name of Pharaoh, open the door!"

The people in the house did not utter a sound.
No one moved; no one opened his mouth.

Aaron was in the attic. He peeked out of the window. What
did he see? One horse belonging to the Egyptians had reared
up on his hind legs.
He was kicking and running wild. Oh! The horse threw off
his rider, neighed, and ran away.

The Egyptians turned to chase the runaway horse.
The people in the house breathed more freely.
The Egyptians had gone.
This time they did not take the baby.
But what would happen the next day?

From that day on, Miriam and Aaron and all their friends stood guard.
If they saw an Egyptian from afar, they would make signs to each other, and Miriam would run shouting to her mother.
"Mother! Egyptians! Hide the baby!"
And Yoheved would snatch up the child and hide him.

Once she hid him in a dovecote, near the baby doves.
Once in the yard, in a broken jug among the water pitchers.
Once in the cellar under the house, and once in a bucket hanging by a rope in the well.

Aaron and Miriam and all the Israelite children tried to fool the Egyptians.

They played tricks to confuse them.

In time of danger they would hide in attics and cellars, in yards and in the houses where there were no children.

They would whine and wail like day-old infants, "ga, ga, ga, ga!"

And the Egyptians would hear them and follow the sounds and say,

"There is a baby here! There is a baby there!"

When the Egyptians would run to the spot, the voice would stop.

The crying of another baby would be heard somewhere else, and the Egyptians would run that way.

This is how they misled the Egyptians and drew them away from the children.

Then the big boys would jump in front of them.

They would stick out their tongues and run away to the fields, meanwhile calling to the Egyptians, "Here I am, catch me! Here I am, catch me!"

In this way they drew them away from the Israelite houses.

But would the tricks always work?

Some day they would be sure to fail.

One night Yoheved and Miriam went down to the river.
By the light of the moon they cut some soft bulrushes and
then returned home.
Yoheved wove a small basket from the reeds.
She covered the outside with pitch and the inside with clay.
She stopped up all the holes and cracks.
Then she lay a soft lamb skin in the basket.
She padded it with a small blanket on which she spread
fragrant myrtle leaves.
She would put in a leaf and cry, put in another leaf and cry.
Her tears flowed into the basket.
She spread out a thin white sheet and laid the baby on it.
The child happily waved his arms and legs, cooed and
laughed.
If he only knew the danger he was in!

The setting sun peeked in through the window and touched
the little boy's head with golden fingers.
The members of the household wiped tears from their faces.
Yoheved put two little pitchers beside him. One contained
milk and the other honey.
She covered the cradle with a lid of reeds woven with many
openings for air.
Fearfully they waited for nightfall.
Miriam, Aaron, and Amram stood guard.

That night they went silently out of the house into the darkness.

Where did they go? To the Nile.

Yoheved walked bent over in the black night.

She was carrying the precious basket.

Slowly and silently they walked. When they saw Egyptian soldiers at the end of an alley they quietly slipped away.

They hid in the shadows of houses and pressed against bushes and hedges.

Now they had to cross a field. The moon was shining. There was light all around.

Please, dear moon!

Hide your face!

Have pity on the baby.

Don't tell our secret.

A cloud covered the face of the moon.

Hurridly they hid in its shadow. They walked in the shadows, always in the shadows.

A breeze came up. Trees rustled and whispered.

They walked on in silence.

They passed the house of the Egyptian overseer, the evil man who supervised the Israelite slaves.

Dogs barked.

A large dog came up to them and sniffed at the basket.

What was in the basket: What was that smell?

The smell of a baby. . .

The dog sniffed, licked, turned around, and walked away.

She was a mother, too. She had her little puppies. The dog took pity on the infant and left.

The Egyptian overseer slept and snored loudly. He did not notice the people passing his house.

And so they went all that night.

When the dawn came, Yoheved put the basket into the water among the reeds under the branches of a willow, a weeping willow shedding tears.

The willow bent its boughs and leaned over the baby like a mother, hiding the basket from all eyes.

Yoheved cried when she left her baby.

Amram and Aaron took her arms and helped her back to their house.

Miriam remained behind to watch over the child.

The dawn's glow shines
on the river,
A weeping willow bows
low over the dark, deep
water
where safe in the shadows
a basket is floating.

A mother's lips move
in fervent prayer,
A sister watches
with bright, dark eyes.

Decend, oh angels,
Watch over this child,
Guard his woven cradle.

A wave of gold
ripples and curls
on the sky-blue water.

Quiet, now, river!
The babe is asleep —
Wings of light enfold him.

Morning came. The Nile was hushed.
Miriam hid behind a broken boat. She watched her little brother, the baby in the basket.

Green waves surged around the ark. Silvery fish swam to and fro.
A crocodile opened its mouth wide, but did not come near the baby.
The reeds rustled in the breeze.
A butterfly hovered above.
A wild duck and her ducklings swam through the water.
A nightingale sang.
A monkey chattered in the distance.
Storks wandered on the river bank hunting for croaking frogs.
The wind whispered in the reeds.
A turtle dove cooed in its nest, "Hagoo, hagoo, hagoo. . ."

Who is that man over there, the one throwing the fishing line into the water?
Who is the fisherman? That is brother Aaron.
And here is another fisherman, throwing in a net. That is Father Amram. He, too, is on guard.
And who is that old man? It is Grandfather roasting fish on the shore.
He has some jugs of wine and a pile of watermelons.
If the Egyptian soldiers come, he will treat them to roasted fish, wine, and watermelons. . . so that Miriam will have time to hide the baby.

It was noon. The sun beat down on everyone's head. The heat was unbearable.

Pharaoh's daughter left the palace to bathe in the river with her maidservants.
What did she see?
In the mirror of the water there was a basket. . . It was rocking on the waves.
A baby's hand peeped over the edge.
The waves revealed their secret.
They told Pharaoh's daughter about the baby. . .
She took pity on the infant. One of her maids drew the cradle out of the water.
She uncovered the cradle and saw —
"Ga, ga ga,. . ."
The baby was crying! It must be hungry, poor little one.
Pharaoh's daughter knew that it was an Israelite baby, the unfortunate child of an unlucky people.
She smiled to him, but he cried and cried and would not stop.
He must be hungry.

They brought a nurse from the palace.
But the baby turned his head away. He shut his tiny lips and refused to suck.
He waved his little fists. A brave child.

Miriam was watching them from a distance. She had seen everything.

She came out of her hiding place and walked over to the baby. He was so happy to see her.

Miriam said to Pharaoh's daughter, "Shall I bring you a woman to suckle the baby?"

"Go, my daughter, and bring me a Hebrew woman to nurse the child."

Miriam ran off and brought — her mother Yoheved.

The baby wriggled its arms and legs and cried with joy. He leaped towards his mother's arms.

He waved his little head and hungrily drank the milk. When he had enough he fell asleep.

Pharaoh's daughter said to Yoheved, "Take this child and nurse him, and I shall pay you."

She gave her baby clothes embroidered in blue and purple, and a crib set with precious stones shaped like the basket. At its front was the Pharaoh's crest.

Then Pharaoh's daughter took a ring from her finger. She gave it to Yoheved and said, "Do not be afraid. Take this child to your home and nurse it. If the Egyptian soldiers come, show them my ring and they will not harm you".

From that day on, the Egyptians did not dare come into Amram's house.

And the boy grew and was good.

Among the Children of Israel people began saying, "The redeemer, the one who will free us, has been born".

And Pharaoh's daughter called the boy Moses (*Mosheh*), because, she said, "I drew him out of the water". (Mosheh means to "draw out" in Hebrew.)

And when Moses became a man, he brought down the ten plagues on Pharaoh, in the name of the God of Israel, and led the Children of Israel out of Egypt, just as the Bible tells.